SCHOLASTIC

Let's Find Out

My REBUS Reader

I0890042

Crunch, Crunch, Apples for Lunch

by Amanda Miller

SCHOLASTIC INC.

New York Toronto London Auckland Sydney New Delhi Hong Kong

A  eats apples.

horse

A  eats apples.

deer

A  eats apples.

bear

A  eats apples.

bird

A  eats apples.

rabbit

A  eats apples.

sheep

Kids eat apples too!